for Mandy

ISBN: 978-0-9528631-7-5

©Marian Bell 2007
Printed in England by
Alpine Press Limited
Kings Langley
WD4 8LF

This book of verse is a forever memory for
Mandy's twin boys Sam and Jake.

I dedicate this book to Mandy, my much loved youngest daughter, who sadly died in 2001 at just 33 years old. She was an inspiration to us all and displayed amazing courage during her brave but all too brief battle with leukaemia.

This book has a special meaning and I hope, in a very small way, it pays tribute to Mandy and provides a lasting memento.

'I treasure every moment we shared together.....'

I give my love and my grateful thanks to:

my husband Terry for his love and
continuing support

my son Gary for his help in editing this book

my family for their understanding and help in
turning a dream into a reality

my sister Sylv for having belief in me at all times
and for just being there

The printing of this book would not have been
possible without the kindness and understanding
of Alpine Press Ltd.

www.alpine-press.co.uk

The front cover is from an original picture by
Morven who deserves a special mention for her
brilliant artwork.

www.artistmovern.co.uk

Mandy's Fairies

by

Marian Bell

Contents

Away with the Fairies

If I could be away
With the fairies one day
To see how they live
All the games they play.
I would watch them fly
And hear how they sing
Could see for myself
A real fairy ring.
Admire all the clothes
Made from petals of flowers
See a magic wish granted
From their special powers.
Learn if stardust really
Does fall from the sky
Watch them ride on a bee
Or a butterfly.
Just one day in fairyland
That would do
If you believe in fairies
You could come too.

Daydreams

One day as I sat dreaming
Shaded by a tree
Had a visit from a fairy
Her name she said Sweet Pea.
She told me she was not alone
Her friends were out to play
One by one she called them
Daisy, Rose and May.
The dresses they were wearing
Made from petals fine as silk
With tiny pearls and droplets
Like bubbles on fresh milk.
Each one of them wore on her head
A brilliant golden crown
Had wings that shone as gossamer
Edged in the finest down.
I woke and looked around me
Sighed if only dreams were true
Glanced down and lying in my lap
Forget-me-nots of blue.

Magical Night

If you look out on a moonlit night
You could be met by a magical sight
Hear tinkling bells, sweet voices sing
Be surprised with a fairy ring.
Like dancing flowers in pretty gowns
Made of silken petals and rosebud crowns
See stardust falling like winter snow
Everything sparkling by the glow worms' glow.
They will laugh and play
Till the break of day
Then as quiet as they came
They will go away.
And it will seem it had never been
Did it really happen or was it a dream?

Washday in Fairyland

I'd like to see what washday's like
In fairyland would you?
Frothy bubbles floating
In a nutshell full of dew.
Underwear the spiders kindly weave
Of the finest lace
Tiny little rosebuds
Sewn in loops around the base.
Dresses are all colours
Of a different hue
Designed from shapes of petals
Only they can do.
Everything is perfumed
With a flower's smell
Some maybe adorned with jewels
Or silver tinkling bells.
Hats might be created
With a twist of flimsy fern
Or a daisy bonnet
Upside down they turn.

Translucent wings are polished
This has to be a must
Carefully re-sprayed again
With a layer of gold dust.
When the washing's finished
Then it's time to dry
So they call their friends the bluebirds
Who patiently wait by.
Each one takes within his beak
An end of swinging vine
Now the fairies have themselves
A perfect washing line.
Everything is gleaming
Freshly in the sun
Are they saying just as we do
So glad washday's done.

Winter's Day

Riding on the snowflakes
As they tumble down
Sounds of tinkling laughter
As they reach the ground.
Sliding down the icicles
Shrieking with delight
Do you get the picture?
Are you imagining the sight?
Boughs of hanging mistletoe
Blow in the winter breeze
As strings of creamy milky pearls
Decorate the trees.
Holly berries ruby red
Glow in the hazy light
Prickly leaves frost sprinkled
Shine as marcasite.
A lovely robin redbreast
Sings a happy song
To give these small folk music
As in turn they skate along.

Acorn bells are ringing
To let everybody know
The sleigh is coming down the hill
Ready here they go.
Tiny little snowballs
Flying through the air
They haven't got a worry
They haven't got a care.
All happy faces beaming
Having so much fun
Of the snow making the best
Before out comes the sun.
We've had a peep at fairyland
Upon a winter's day
But in a moment like our dream
It soon will melt away.

Poppy's Gown

The silkworms are weaving
Their finest rich thread
A gown has been ordered
In the reddest of red.
Blackcurrant buttons
Shine ebony black
To begin at the neck
And run right down the back.
The skirt to be made up
Of delicate folds
With a bodice encrusted
In silvers and golds.
Such a beautiful gown
Never could have a copy
It's being specially designed
For a fairy named Poppy.
If you're lucky might see her
On a bright sunny day
Dancing in cornfields
Is where she likes to play.
So keep your eyes open
Don't forget what I've said
Look out for the fairy
Named Poppy in red.

Fairyland Wish

In the land of fairies
Where everything is small
People the size of thumbnails
Houses are toadstools.
Clothes are made from flower petals
Two leaves a pair of shoes
All the things of nature
Only tools they use.
A rose that is just blooming
Makes a cosy bed
Where any tired fairy
Can lay her sleepy head.
Birds and bees provide their music
Entertainment comes for free
All medicines provided
By friendly doctor bee.
In the land of fairies
Sounds the perfect place to me
If only I could make a wish
That is where I'd be.

The Party

The fairies are having a party
All meeting up for tea
Hundreds of them arriving
Faces all smiling with glee.
Pippin the pixie is usher
Guiding everyone to their chair
Every member of fairyland
Is going to be there.
Nutshells are lit as lanterns
Brightly adorning the trees
Garlands of pretty wild flowers
Gently sway in the breeze.
A silver trail covers the tables
Patterned as if in braille
To make a perfect tablecloth
Lovingly designed by a snail.
The tiniest fruit pies seen ever
And cakes of caraway seed
The bees provided the honey on crumbs
With drinks to follow of mead.
A cake made of fresh ripe berries
Stands proud in the centre place
On layer piled upon layer
Of a succulent honeycomb base.

Now the eating is over
The dance is about to begin
They all join hands in a circle
To form the fairy ring.
Stardust will now begin falling
And gently cover the floor
This is the exciting moment
They all have waited for.
Music is filling the air now
By a flute made out of straw
A picture of happy faces
Could anyone else ask for more?
What a wonderful party
Were you watching?
Did you see?
I wish I was a fairy
And they had invited me.

Shared Moment

While dozing alone in my armchair
Watching the firelight glow
Something bright and shiny caught my eye
What it was I didn't know.
Gingerly I crept over
To take a closer look
There sat the tiniest person
Reading a petal leafed book.
She looked up at me shyly
With eyes of bright sapphire blue
Said wonder if you can help me?
Got a problem, don't know what to do.
In the palm of her hand she had moonbeams
In your garden these I have to sow
To give you some lovely spring flowers
To cheer you up after winter's snow.
The queen of the fairies has ordered
A carpet of colour for you
But I tripped and fell in a puddle
Look my dress and my wings are wet through.
So if I could share your fire
Let my page of instructions dry
This moment of magic just shared with you
Will last forever but I must fly.

Sophie May

I met a little fairy
Just the other day
I asked her what her name was
She answered Sophie May.
Said she'd been told to visit
Time with me would like to spend
Thought I looked lost and lonely
Could she be my friend?
I nodded very cautiously
Didn't understand at all
She touched me with a little wand
Suddenly I too was small.
A few little surprises
I have for you in store
Realised that I was flying
My feet no longer on the floor.
Up and up we floated
High up in the sky
Landed on a fluffy cloud
That was passing by.
Way above the houses
Way up above the trees
Slowly we just sailed along
Taken by the breeze.
She showed me magic places
I had never seen before
But as quickly as it started
I was back outside my door.

Can You Imagine?

Can you imagine a violet
Worn as a tiny gown,
A spider's web all sprinkled with dew
Woven into a crown?
Can you imagine snowdrop shoes
On feet that are very small,
Can you imagine anyone
Who could be wearing them at all?
Can you imagine a bluebell
Carried as a shining light,
Or a daisy for a parasol
To shield the bright sunlight?
Can you imagine a buttercup
Holding afternoon tea,
Can you imagine any place
Where this you would see?
Can you imagine a dark night
When the moon is shining bright,
And lots of little people
Have fun to their hearts delight?
Can you imagine music played
On a harp made from blades of grass,
Can you imagine dancing
Underneath falling stars?
Can you imagine this picture
This wonderful magical scene,
Do you believe in fairies
For fairyland's where you have been?

The Snow Fairy

Not many see the Snow Fairy
On a cold and wintry night
In a dress made from lily petals
Of the whitest white.
Jack Frost has sprinkled on it
A pattern finer than lace
A hat of doves' soft feathers
Frames her pretty face.
With hair hanging down in ringlets
She glides with elegant grace
On her feet she wears cut glass slippers
Stars are shining all over the place.
Take a look for yourself as snow's falling
Heavily from the skies
You may be one of the lucky ones
But will you believe your eyes?

Buttercup

You may see her on a summer's day
In a sunshine yellow gown
On her head she will be wearing
A lovely golden crown.
Her legs are clad in stockings
Of a pretty green
On her feet are satin slippers
The tiniest ever seen.
She will dance among the daisies
In your garden on the grass
And everywhere she passes
Sets a new seed as she laughs.
This is such a happy person
Brightly lights a garden up
Who is this little fairy?
Why of course it's Buttercup.

The Shoemaker

Binky is the cobbler
Who makes the fairies' shoes
He will make them any colour
Or whatever style they choose.
He creates from many flowers
With a pretty frilly edge
Or boots which button up the front
On berries picked from the hedge.
Should a bow-tie be needed
It is tied with a blade of grass
Or for a special occasion
Slippers translucent as glass.
Clogs will be designed special
Etched out of a small nutshell
These orders would be from the pixies
Who live in fairyland as well.
He has his little workshop
Beneath the old oak tree
A sign hangs up above the door
All shoes hand made by me.

The Visit

I dreamt I saw a fairy
Peep from behind a tree
Wondered what she is looking at
Is she watching me?
I heard a sweet voice call my name
A finger beckoned me
So I followed silently
Quiet as I could be.
All at once around me
Fairies everywhere
In the prettiest colours
Dewdrop jewels in their hair.
Saw tables made of toadstools
Daisy cushions for a chair
A nutshell as a cradle
A baby fairy lying there.
Then the queen of fairies
Said there's something you should know
What you see must be a secret
Promise me before you go.

We saw you looked unhappy
And know you're feeling sad
When you wake up you are sure to think
Is this a dream I've had?
They said been asked to visit
By someone special who I knew
If your belief is strong enough
Anything is true.
Anyone who sees our fairy ring
Are expertly picked by hand
You were chosen by a loved one
For a look at fairyland.
The magic I was shown there
Never will be told
But will stay with me forever
Till I'm very, very old.

Imagination

In among your flowers
Could be a hidden fairy's throne
I am told these are the places
A fairy chooses for a home.
It could be in a bluebell
Or the centre of a rose
How many of them live there?
Don't think anybody knows.
They come out when no-one's looking
To have fun, play, sing and dance
Dressed in the brightest colours
Silver wings spread to enhance.
Their world is known as wonderland
Where stardust falls as snow
But only through imagination
Are we allowed to go.

Playtime

Come and watch the fairies playing
Join in with their fun
See them playing peek-a-boo
From behind the sun.
They laugh while swinging on the stars
Up in the sky at night
Or catch me round and round the moon
Squealing in delight.
The rainbow is a perfect slide
With colours all ablaze
They dance among the flowers
On sunny summer days.
Tiny legs are skipping
Catkin tails are used as rope
The wings of sycamore pods
Skis for slipping down a slope.
There's hide and seek in roots of trees
Or down a rabbit hole
Berries make good marbles
Or a ball to roll.
I've painted you a picture
Of games the fairies play
Hope it's brought to you some magic
And brightened up your day.

Special Fairy

A carpet of red rose petals
Sprayed with diamond dew
Leads to a throne of flowers
To welcome a fairy new.
Around it there shines a halo
Made from the rainbow bright
With a sprinkling of tiny moonbeams
To give it an extra light.
A beautiful cushion of daisies
And carried upon it a crown
Created from purple violets
And edged in a fine white down.
A magic wand lies beside it
With a star chosen from the sky
The awaited moment arrives now
As the queen of fairies glides by.
They all gather round in a circle
A dream is about to come true
She has chosen a special fairy
That special fairy is you.

Surprise Visit

A fairy tapped upon the glass
Of my window pane
Help, I am in a muddle
Let me in I will explain.
She climbed up and sat on my finger
Pretty face full of concern
Her little limbs were shaking
What was wrong was yet to learn.
She'd been hiding in the flowers
From a cat had got a fright
I asked how long she'd been there
On a sob, most of the night.
A tiny tear rolled down her cheek
Plopped on her violet dress
I whispered softly to her
How can I help you best?
If you could kindly lift me
Into Mr Robin's nest
He will get me safely home
And I'll leave you to rest.
So I did just as she asked
Turned back towards my door
Where pinned upon it was a note
Granted luck forever more.

Anemone

Here comes the fairy windflower
Anemone was named
Stands tall in all her glory
For her beauty she is famed.
Her dark eyes are the deepest
Black as any seen
The colours of her dresses
Fit only for a queen.
Each petal one of purple silk
Or very royal red
As the breeze blows lightly
Nods proudly with her head.
She is one of the prettiest
Nature could ever preen
If you're lucky enough to meet her
Will know just what I mean.

Primrose

Primrose is a pretty fairy
In yellow she is dressed
Every single petal
Has been separately pressed.
She is delicate of nature
And is always very good
You can find her flowers growing
Nestled somewhere in the wood.
Green leaves grow around her
Protecting her from harm
Adding to her beauty
Also giving extra charm.
If you go out country walking
In the springtime of the year
Keep your eyes wide open
Fairy Primrose may appear.

Fairy Bluebell

A pointed cap fitted like a crown
Skirt with tiny bells hanging down
Silken petals of sapphire blue
Gossamer wings you can almost see through.
Her feet are clad in tiny glass shoes
They sparkle like crystal, all coloured hues
The woods are where she will dance all day
Waving magic wand dust along the way.
From this masses of flowers appear
Like a great big carpet year after year
She will finish them off with a scented dew
This is Fairy Bluebell's gift to you.

Pure Honesty

In a silver white dress
Pure silk petals and lace
Coils of bright copper curls
Cascade a sweet face.
Round her neck hangs a necklace
A small cross and chain
Rose thorns in a kiss
Threaded on drops of rain.
Her head is adorned
With a most special crown
It's the bloom of a lily
Turned upside down.
From the hem of her gown
Tiny pink toes pop out
A fairy of beauty
Without any doubt.
I don't know her name
But think you'll agree
With the one I have chosen
Pure Honesty.

Doc the Pixie

Doc the Pixie
Lives up in the hills
With potions and lotions
He cures many ills.
The oldest of fairies
Made on him a call
Said I'm feeling rhuematicy
Can't fly at all.
So he mixed up a remedy
Now let me see
We'll have oil from an olbas
And the sting from a bee.
Then he tapped it three times
Whispered fiddle-de-dee
All of a sudden
From all pain she was free.

Next came Pru the fairy
Looking tired and worn
Had fallen into bramble
Got her tiny wing torn.
He smiled at her kindly
Oh it's nought but a scratch
I'll soon fix this up
With a spider web patch.
Again tapped it three times
Whispered fiddle-de-do
When Pru looked at her wing
It was perfect as new.
How does he do it?
I wish I could tell
It's a secret the magic
Of Doc's pixie spell.

Peace

Long curly eyelashes
Small turned up nose
A gown of pink flounces
Frilled layers in rows.
A small face surrounded
In gold feathery hair
Wherever she goes
Perfume follows her there.
Soft wings like a butterfly
Tinted with green
A sprinkling of stardust
To add extra sheen.
Lips sweet as a cherry
Peach blush on her cheeks
This fairy brings flowers
The roses called Peace.

Penny

Her name is Penny the fairy
Chestnut eyes, long copper hair
Wrote her order to the pixie tailor
For brand new winter wear.
Red berries she chose for a bonnet
Edged in fern of dark emerald green
Boots softly lined with duck-down
To keep small feet warm and clean.
A special dress to be made up
From leaves russet, orange and gold
Decorated with bright diamond dew drops
Stitched carefully to every fold.
Disguised in her autumn colours
In woodland she dances free
You may hear her tinkling laughter
In foliage underneath a tree.
If you visit make sure you are quiet
And tread very carefully
For this little fairy Penny
Is too small for you to see.

Sweet Melody

Eyes as green as emeralds
Hair like polished jet
A circle of orange blossoms
Upon her head is set.
Layered skirt, bright orange petals
Bodice butter cream
Scalloped wings of cut-glass
Shimmer colours of moonbeam.
As I watched she started singing
In a voice clear as could be
The words she told was the fairy
Known as Sweet Melody.

Twinkle

I'd like you to meet Twinkle
The fairy of the night
She dances round the hazy moon
To make the dark sky bright.
In and out among the clouds
She gaily sprinkles stars
All along the Milky Way
To Jupiter and Mars.
Then she flies down to the ground
Still more work to be done
Scattering fresh scented dew
Before out comes the sun.
Puts jewels on the flowers
To make the petals glow
And when the task is over
Morning breaks it's time to go.

Anita

On a cabbage rose bed
In a very dark red
A tiny wee fairy
Has laid down her head.
Her black hair is fanned out
Like a raven bird's wing
The smile on her lips
Says a sweet dream she's in.
Her dress is the shade
Of creamy white milk
Round the hem yellow buttercups
Petals of silk.
On her wrist wears a bracelet
Of words Fairy Anita
I wish she would wake up
I'd so love to meet her.

Bright Little Star

She uses her needles
Made from splinters of reeds
Then polishes berries
To a clear shine like beads.
Thorns picked from the hedgerow
Pin her pattern in place
Her friend Mr Spider
Weaves for her fine lace.
Gets threads from the silkworm
To stitch them all up
Crosses sycamore wings
Scissors if she must cut.
Then her small nimble fingers
Will put them together
Making one of the loveliest
Dresses seen ever.
Like glass it will sparkle
And glow out a light
You may see her and make a wish
On a dark night.
She is one of the best known
Of fairies by far
A favourite of everyone
Bright Little Star.

Wise Old Fairy

She sits upon a throne built up
Of burnished copper gold
The wisest of all fairies
She is very, very old.
I'm told she's lived in Fairyland
A thousand years or more
Everyone who lives there
Is welcome at her door.
They all pay her a visit
To tell about their day
What they have been doing
And the games they play.
She'll ask if they've been extra good
Or have gone astray
If anything is worrying them
In her kindly way.

She always has a listening ear
Offers good advice
Never loses patience
Is always sweet and nice.
Her hair is sparkling silver
Twinkly eyes a brilliant blue
The smile she smiles could melt away
The coldest heart it's true.
A bag of seeds she gives each one
As they say goodbye
With a message you will scatter these
Everywhere you fly.
Out of these good things of nature
Will forever grow
To let the magic love of fairies
Everybody know.

The Scruffy Pixie

Simon the scruffy pixie
Has a chubby grubby face
His hair is long and straggly
Sometimes looks a disgrace.
With buttons off his jacket
Patches covering his clothes
Boots all worn and holey
Peeping through his toes.
Doesn't take a bath too often
So you couldn't call him clean
A follower of fashion
Definitely not his scene.
He never gets embarrassed
Full of confidence and bold
But you just can't help but like him
Behind it all a heart of gold.

Marigold

Marigold the fairy
Makes her own ray of sun
All around the gardens
This little one will run.
Her wings are golden satin
With a shiny lustrous sheen
Hazel eyes peep shyly
Beneath longest lashes seen.
Skin soft and smooth as velvet
On her cheeks a rosy glow
A smile with red lips parted
Tiny teeth like pearl drops show.
In a dress of daisy petals
So bright they almost glare
All been freshly dyed
To match her mop of orange hair.
She may run a little wildly
Also be a bit don't care
But she's full of life and colour
So I'm sure she's welcome there.

Spring Clean

Spring Fairy put up a notice
It's time to clean today
Turn out all the feathers
From your old duvet.
Choose sheets of soft silk petals
Put freshly on your beds
Make brand new fluffy pillows
On which to lay your heads.
All windows need replacing
From a dragon fly's clear wings
Re-hang bright leafy curtains
Scatter round some pretty things.
Polish all your furniture
And make it really shine
Rubbing in some beeswax
Will help to do this fine.
Toadstools need re-painting
Don't forget to shake your mats
When all the work's completed
Then everyone relax.

Fairy Daffodil

In a bright yellow bonnet
With a scalloped edged brim
Tied in a satin bow
Under her chin.
Matching the colour
A crinoline gown
Showing lace of her petticoat
Beneath hanging down.
She creeps round the garden
Tiny steps tippy-toe
Whispers soft to her flowers
Wake up time to grow.
Put on your best dresses
Display all your frills
Dance in all your glory
My daffodils.

Pip the Pixie

Underneath the toadstool
Pip the Pixie's sat
Spending every hour each day
Eating growing fat.
All Fairyland was worried
Were afraid that he would bust
So decided all together
To help him was a must.
They gathered at a meeting
Came up with a secret plan
This way they decided
To help the podgy man.
In pairs they all would line up
From mountain top to glen
To each other roll Pip to and fro
Then pass him on again.
They knew this was a lesson
Must be taught to him
By the time he reached the bottom
He'd feel very sick but slim.

Champagne Rose

There's a fairy wildly dancing
Out in the pouring rain
You can hear her shrieks of laughter
As she enjoys her game.
There are bubbles from the raindrops
Flying everywhere
Black corkscrew curls are bobbing
In her soaking hair.
She carries an umbrella
Edged with rainbow trims
She twists it and she twirls it
Like a magic top it spins.
She jumps in every puddle
Splashing her nice pink clothes
I don't know what her name is
But I'll call her Champagne Rose.

Flossie

Have you met Flossie the Fairy?
Velvet skin and eyes of blue
Beneath long spidery lashes
She'll peep shyly up at you.
Her gold straw hair shines brightly
Which is carefully wound into a plait
Then twisted round and round her head
In the shape of a pretty hat.
Her dress is of many colours
From feathers of softest down
Looks like a tiny powder puff
Bobbing along the ground.
She might come and visit your garden
And stop for a sip of dew
I think she's a special fairy
Perhaps you will think so too.

Red Rose

A sweet little fairy
We know of as Rose
Brings a message unspoken
In the folds of her clothes.
It tells of endearment
How close one's held near
The deepest of feelings
All wrapped up in here.
From a bud all her secrets
Begin to unfold
Exposing a story intended be told.
As slowly she blooms
Her deep red petals part
Show the meaning within them
Love right from the heart.

Mischievous Pixie

Underneath the hedgerow
Is where this pixie plays
Getting up to mischief
Is how he spends his days.
Tormenting the fairies
Throwing berries from the trees
Shaking bags of pollen
Making them all sneeze.
Setting up his twig traps
With nasty prickly thorn
Then he laughs until he cries
When on them dresses torn.
His mind is always busy
What trick can he do next?
He's made the fairies angry
Got them very vexed.

So they have got together
Decided on a scheme
Gave Pixie his own medicine
So he wouldn't be so mean.
Quietly they crept up
While he slept in his bed
Painted stripes upon his face
Yellow, orange, red.
Tied his feet together
With a length of swinging vine
Then they filled his boots up
With elderberry wine.
Wonder if he learnt his lesson
When he woke up next day
Or did he sulk, pack all his bags
And simply move away.

Sylvia the Dreamer

If you have a wish
You want to come true
Sylvia the Dreamer
Is the fairy for you.
She says nothing's impossible
Just get a plan
Never say I can't do
But always yes I can.
Don't give up, must persevere
She'll whisper in your ear
Now you have travelled this far
Got to your goal so near.
If you want something bad enough
Your star will shine for you
A touch from Sylvia the Dreamer's wand
Who knows what you can do.

Ginny

They call her Creeping Ginny
Friendly fairy of the vine
Playing games together
They got along just fine.
Ladders made of twisted stems
On fences over walls
Laughing, clinging to each other
In case one of them falls.
Sometimes the vine would make a swing
For little Ginny's fun
Through summer they could laze all day
And just enjoy the sun.
But now autumn is coming
There's work to do instead
All the leaves now growing green
Must be coloured brightest red.
In weeks the job was finished
No more paint left to spray
Vine curled up and went to sleep
While Ginny crept away.

The Gathering

All the fairies from each season congregate today
Gathering together to attend a big display.
There's Hyacinth and Snowdrop, Lily, Daisy, May
Violet and Primrose, Bluebell's on her way.
Red Peony and Hollyhock, Morning Glory too
All donned in their best dresses, coming to this special do.
Roses in all colours, sweet scented by the dew
Chrysanthemum and Black Eyed Suzie, Forget-Me-Nots of blue.
All different shades of pansies, sweet pea, delightful smell
Pinks, Carnations, Dahlias are looking good as well.
Lily of the Valley, Tulips, Yellow Daffodils
Still they are arriving, over mountain, vales and hills.
The blossoms of the Lilac, Magnolia, Cherry Tree
On the breeze the sounds of laughter, faces full of glee.
I'd like to name each one but there are hundreds in the queue
Wish you could see this picture - it's a fairytale come true.